TOP
SACRED

TOP
SACRED

by
Hugh Burnett

The Dial Press

New York 1961

Those drawings which first appeared in the
New Statesman
are reproduced by courtesy of the Editor

To Thomas,
who had some doubts.

TOP
SACRED

'I think you've done it up awfully well!'

'Good gracious! Oh dear!! My Oh My!!!'

'For ever and ever Amen. Full stop. Paragraph.
Big Roman R with gilt bits around the edge. . . .'

'If you need anything, just ring.'

'Short top and sides, please.'

'I washed it last night and I can't
do a thing with it.'

'Terribly boring silly plot!'

'No, thanks — I've read it!'

'I'm afraid we're already committed.'

. . . and stop calling me Dad!'

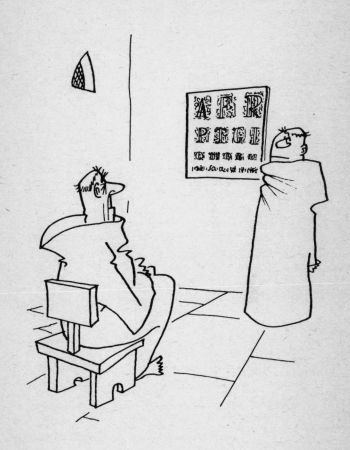

'Abbot, Cardinal, Bishop, Pope....'

'Now, watch the angel!'

'If you think I'm going to own up to a broken Madonna you must believe in miracles!'

'How many candles do you reckon
I could buy with $75,000?'

'Please can Gilbert come out to pray?'

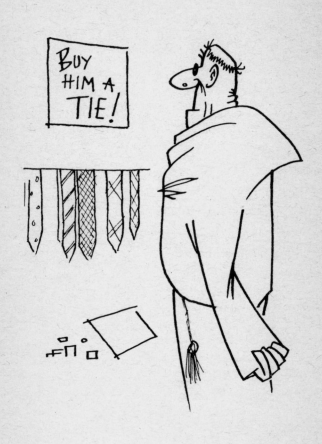

'Happy birthday, dear Abbot,
happy birthday to you!'

'I've put "Best wishes from
all the lads in Cell 11."'

'Hot as what?'

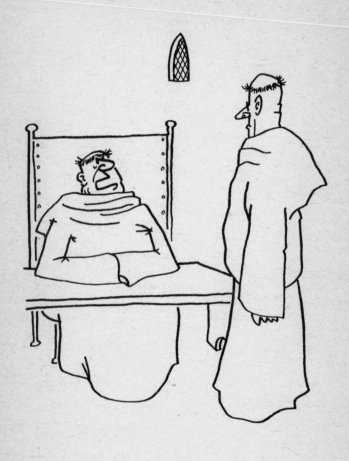

'Home rule, Father O'Reilly, is one of the things we're supposed to have left behind us!'

'Tie them I did, but darned if I can remember
what they're to remind me of!'

'Somebody round here's been taking more than
his fair share of loaves and fishes!'

'He's been in there singing hymns
for the last hour and a half!'

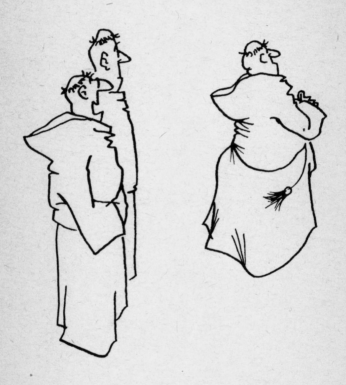

'It's not only his mind that's been broadened
by years of contemplation!'

'Prayer— and a liberal sprinkling of fertiliser!'

'You can't even get a good argument
around here — everybody agrees with you!'

'Giving up worldly goods was easy for me —
I was broke!'

'Brother Timothy's got some very bad habits.'

'Trouble is I enjoy doing without things!'

'One lucky break for me was a rather late
conversion from the fleshpots!'

'The Abbot said I could keep it until such time
as I actually came to like it.'

'Am I allowed to try to win?'

'I've invented a wonderful new
non-labor-saving method!'

'For Lent I'm giving up carbohydrates!'

'It fits beautifully, but can I have something a little more uncomfortable?'

'I regret to say I had rather
an enjoyable day!'

'A very serious thing happened to me
on my way here tonight.'

'You'd think one of them would have hit upon
the idea of being pious and comfortable!'

'If they'd change the cook I'd give up
my fasting!'

'Is an indigestion tablet cheating?'

'Cold snap or not — hot water bottles are out!'

'I'm looking for a drip-dry hair shirt.'

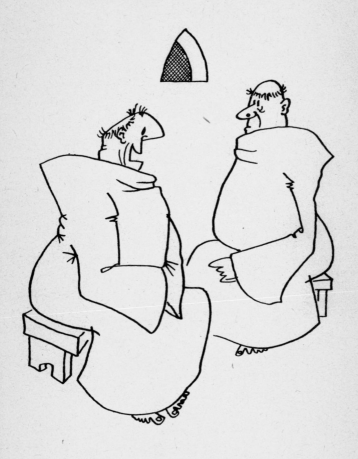

'Sometimes I ask myself what I've done
to deserve so much unhappiness.'

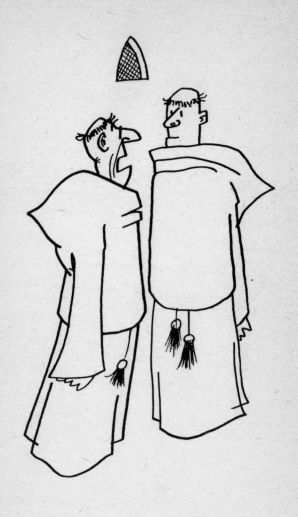

'I've run out of things to give up!'

'More than anything else in the whole world,
I miss my trousers.'

'All this "get thee behind me Satan" stuff
gives me a shocking feeling of being followed!'

'I keep dreaming of black sheep!'

'It's on the index — but I'm reading it
as a self-imposed penance.'

'No, no, my dear chap — you're supposed
to list your own faults!'

'Shall I repent first, or will you?'

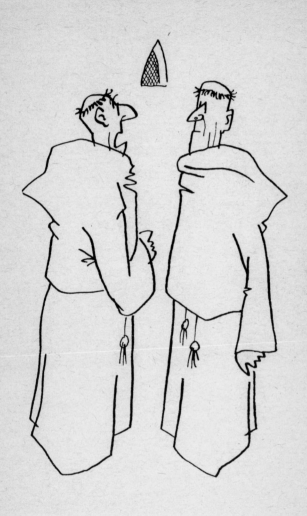

'I keep getting doubts about my doubts!'

'I'm a very angry young monk.'

'Okay, it's a miracle — but why be
so surprised?'

'Quite frankly marriage guidance isn't one
of my strong points.'

'My confessor doesn't understand me.'

'It was all right for St. Francis — but I
wouldn't know what to say to a bird.'

'Brother Erasmus is mystically inclined.'

'By far and away he's our oldest relic.'

'Do you think I like it up here?'

'It didn't work!'

'Caspar's angel-watching.'

'He's going to find it harder than most,
resurrecting through all that!'

'And are there real pearls on the gate?'

BLESS
THIS
MONASTERY

THE
END